100 Books You
Really Should Read

*All booklets are published thanks to the
generous support of the members of the
Catholic Truth Society*

CATHOLIC TRUTH SOCIETY
PUBLISHERS TO THE HOLY SEE

Contents

How to use this Guide

So often people looking for something good to read just don't know where to start, nor have any idea of the treasure chest of Catholic (Christian) literature that is available. This booklet contains a list of 100 books which you might like to get to know about - especially if you're someone who just wants to make a start and find out more about your Christian faith and heritage.

We asked around 25 contributors to list some of the best ten books they'd ever read, really loved and thought valuable. We asked them specifically for the books they would recommend to anyone else wanting to enrich their Catholic and Christian faith through their general reading – without needing to be a great expert.

These 100 suggestions for reading are not intended to be a definitive or exhaustive list. It's just a start, a useful list drawn up for you by interested friends who realise how important broadening the mind and good reading is. The 100 books span biography, fiction, history, some general spiritual reading, and a bit of theology and teaching – which is not a bad list to start with. Hopefully, it should give you a taste of the wealth of good literature there is about Christianity, and Catholicism in particular.

The idea is to browse through and see what takes your interest: alternatively you may be looking for a particular book or author and prefer to scan the two indexes at the back: - either way, dip in!

Most of the books mentioned here are in print, but to help users we devised two symbols to give an idea of how popular some books are, and how available they are today. So, an entry marked * is one recommended by several contributors; (P) indicates that a book may be out of print, but certainly remains obtainable with some sensible searching.

Biography

1. A Good Man in Evil Times: The unknown hero who saved countless lives in World War II, by José-Alain Fralon (2000, Viking; transl. Peter Graham). A Catholic Portuguese diplomat in Bordeaux when the Nazis invaded France in 1940, Aristides de Sousa Mendes disobeyed his country's orders to stop issuing visas to Jews desperate to escape. He knew he was risking his career, but chose to act in accordance with his Christian faith. As a result, he was dismissed from the diplomatic service without a pension, unable to get any other job, and died in abject poverty. In some respects his life was not exemplary, but his courage in obeying the voice of his conscience, and the way he kept his promise to Jewish refugees, "I'll save you all!" make him a truly memorable figure. The only pity about this book is that the writer, not a Catholic, does not really do justice to his subject's lively faith and deep religious devotion.

2. A Life with Karol: My forty-year friendship with the man who became Pope, by Stanislaw Dziwisz (2008, Doubleday). Father Stanislaw (now Cardinal) Dziwisz became secretary to the then Archbishop Wojtyla of Krakow in 1966. He remained at his side until Pope John Paul II died in 2005. From this privileged position, Dziwisz chronicles the struggles of Wojtyla's life as a determined Bishop under the Communist regime in Poland, his election to the papacy in October 1978, the 1981 assassination attempt and his reaction to it, his visits to his native land before and after the collapse of Eastern bloc Communism, his opposition to the war against Iraq, and the truly heroic way he faced his final sickness and death.

3.   A Long Retreat, by Andrew Krivak (2008, Farrar, Straus and Giroux; autobiography). Krivak, brought up in a mid-West American Catholic family with Ruthenian roots, spent seven years as a Jesuit novice. He writes about this experience with neither sentimentality nor bitterness in this exquisitely-written book, which one reviewer described as 'the best spiritual memoir I have read since Thomas Merton's *Seven Storey Mountain*'.

4.   Apologia Pro Vita Sua, by Cardinal John Henry Newman * (First pub. 1864, 1913 OUP, many eds; autobiography /spirituality). Unquestionably one of the greatest autobiographies in English written by one of the greatest English Catholics. Twenty years after his conversion to Catholicism, Newman managed to write a deep, searching autobiography without once sounding either conceited or self-centred. Even when refuting the accusations of his attackers he never falls into spite or bitterness. His sincerity, love for the truth, and above all his love for God, are the lasting impressions made by this "History of my religious opinions", all conveyed in clear, readable English prose. The resulting book is not only a vivid, spiritual self-portrait of one of the leading religious figures of 19th Century Britain, but a compelling argument in favour of the truth of the Catholic Faith.

5.   Beethovan: His spiritual development, by J.W.N. Sullivan (1960, Random House; spiritual biography, Allen and Unwin; spiritual biography). Music can be a powerful reminder of the reality of the spiritual. Beethovan was, of course, a Catholic and his greatest music includes a glorious setting of the Mass, written during his final years. This book by Sullivan explores Beethovan's religious beliefs and shows us, through his life, letters, and a consideration of his music, how he found God even through the intense difficulties and suffering he endured because of his deafness and loneliness.

6.   Before the Dawn, by Eugenio Zolli (1954, Sheed and Ward; also published as *Why I Became a Catholic*; other eds. available). Part of the value of this autobiography is the light it sheds on Jewish life and thinking in the mid-twentieth century, helping towards an understanding of current Catholic-Jewish dialogue. The author was Chief Rabbi of Rome before and during World War II. At the end of it, as the result of a long process of thought, prayer and inspiration that had started in his childhood, motivated first and foremost by simple love of Jesus Christ, he was baptized a Catholic, taking the Christian name of the Pope, Pius XII (Eugenio Pacelli). **(P)**

7.   Confessions of a Convert, by Robert Hugh Benson (1913; 1991, Fisher Press; autobiography). Robert Hugh Benson, younger son of a famous Archbishop of Canterbury and of a very talented family, first took Orders in the Anglican Church and then, amid much publicity, became a Roman Catholic in 1903 and, not long afterwards, a Catholic priest. This autobiographical book reveals his spiritual journey and with great humility shows that in all honesty, he had to become a Catholic. The *Confessions* are very explicit on his intellectual journey into the Catholic Church and the many efforts by leading Anglican churchmen of renown and scholarship, as well as his family, to dissuade him. His journey to the Middle East to recuperate after an illness first brought him face to face with the universality of the Catholic Church and the smallness and restricted geographical extension of the Anglican communion.

The book is amazingly up to date on the concern for the directions in which the Anglican Church was moving at the time and also the general malaise among many Anglicans. Over a hundred years later the concerns are even more relevant.

8. Edmund Campion, by Evelyn Waugh * (1935; var. editions; 2005, Ignatius Press; biography). St Edmund Campion was one of the most distinguished of the Catholic priests and laypeople who suffered martyrdom under Queen Elizabeth. Had he remained in the established church, he would certainly have won preferment; but he sacrificed all this to train for the priesthood with the Jesuits. He was reconciled to the forbidden religion while at Oxford and followed William Allen into exile. He joined the Society of Jesus and was sent to teach in Prague. After some years there he was sent on "the English mission" which meant almost certain martyrdom. His wit, courage and tenacity were put to the test in the following few years, which culminated in his being betrayed, and hanged, drawn and quartered at Tyburn in 1581. Waugh concludes his preface to the 1946 edition, "The haunted, trapped, murdered priest is our contemporary, and Campion's voice sounds to us across the centuries as though he were walking at our elbow." This brief but lucid biography of a great English gentleman, scholar and saint was written in 1935 not after Waugh's conversion to Catholicism: it captures so well the atmosphere of fear and courage in which Campion ministered when he returned to England, and he gives fine examples of Campion's own writings. Campion's trial and brutal execution is movingly described.

9. From Gangland to Promised Land, by John Pridmore with Greg Watts (2002, DLT; 2004, Xt3Media). John Pridmore tells us his amazing, dramatic and explicit story which starts in the violent and murky shadows of East End gangster land. He then leads us, via a powerful experience of God's love, through his struggling and striving to get out of his gangster life and make amends in finding his true vocation to serve the Lord. One of the loveliest moments is having had his initial encounter with the Lord, he needed to tell someone immediately. So at 1.30 am he rang his mother's doorbell, and when she answered he blurted out, "Mum, I think I've found God!" "What, at 1.30 in the morning?", as only a mother can in circumstances like this! He is now a well known national and international evangelist. A gritty, inspiring read, which has changed many people's lives.

10. He Leadeth Me, by Walter Ciszek SJ (1995, Ignatius Press). Fr Walter Ciszek dreamed of doing missionary work in Russia. He worked hard to master the language but when the opportunity came he was soon arrested and charged with espionage. Spending over twenty years in prison and labour camps, Ciszek relied upon the foundations of the spiritual life which he had learned in his Jesuit formation. Learning to trust in God and sanctify the ordinary things of each day, Ciszek began a lively apostolic work among his fellow prisoners. This powerful account of his experiences sheds new light on prayer, work and the meaning of the Mass.

11. Hugh Dormer's Diaries, by Hugh Dormer (1947; 1998, Fisher Press; diaries). First published in 1947 and running to four reprints at the time, *Hugh Dormer's Diaries* cover the period in his life from April 1943 till his death in July 1944. The diaries are dedicated to his mother so that, should he be killed, she would know what he did during the war. A young man in his early twenties, he was drafted from his regiment to join the SOE (Special Operations Executive) and parachuted into France twice for sabotage work. His diary from April to September 1943 covers his dangerous work both in France, carrying out the objectives and escaping back to England over the Pyrenees, trying to avoid capture and death. It brings alive the hazards, fear, loss, great physical pain, courage, determination and idealism of this practical young leader of a group, while showing his deep Catholic faith which he writes about with great simplicity. The period from September till his death is more personal, revealing his motives for wanting to go back to his army unit and be with his soldiers rather than doing sabotage activity. His family motto was "What God wills, I will". The last entries of this part of the *Diaries* show his faith and ideals and how he put the motto into practice.

12. In the Shadow of His Wings, by Gereon Goldmann * (1964, 2000, Ignatius Press). The story-line of this autobiography reads like pure fiction. Karl Goldmann was an unlikely Franciscan, and the Franciscan Brother Gereon Goldmann was a still more unlikely German soldier. He cheerfully risked his life hundreds of times to preserve his commitment to God, defying the Nazis even when conscripted into the SS, never killed or wronged anyone, and was ordained to the priesthood in a prison camp. War is insane; good can emerge even from the rubble of evil. We are reminded just how hard it was for conscientious Catholics under the Nazi regime. It is the story of how God acts subtly through the crooked lines of human depravity and sin. Hope is possible even in the most extraordinary moments of despair. Dedicated throughout to spreading the Gospel, he went to Japan after the war and earned himself the title "the Rag-picker of Tokyo" by his efforts to set up charitable institutions for the poor. This book gives you a lot to think about.

13. Letters from a Lost Generation: First World War letters of Vera Brittain and four friends, ed. by Alan Bishop and Mark Bostridge (1998, Little, Brown and Co). In our national collective memory, the thousands and thousands of young men slaughtered in the Great War, each one irreplaceable and loved and important, stand out starkly. The rows of white crosses in those huge war cemeteries across what was once the Western Front, the names on the Menin Gate and carved into the granite of war memorials in every suburb and village, the monuments in churches and schools and the hospitals and halls built in their memory – these have become part of the fabric of the lives of subsequent generations but they can't convey the tragedy of it all, the loss, the heartbreak. Vera Brittain lost a fiancé, a brother, and close friends – these letters tell the story.

14. Life of Thomas More, by Peter Ackroyd * (1999, Knopf Publishing Group; biography). If you love both Catholic history and London, this is an ideal biography. The best parts are the early chapters which recount More's schooldays in late medieval London - so vivid you can almost smell the place - and his early training in the law where fluency in Latin, Norman French and English was required. The chapters outlining the humanistic debates of the period are difficult but rewarding and the story of More's trial, incarceration and execution are movingly told. Peter Ackroyd's gift is to write gripping, well-researched history. His facts are abundant and told with a zest. Thomas More is noble, humble, witty, self-sacrificing and gripped by a desire to do no wrong in a Catholic way in a world bursting with Machiavellian and Protestant ideas.

15. Literary Converts: Spiritual inspiration in an age of unbelief, by Joseph Pearce * (1999, HarperCollins). The story of the many English literary and theatrical figures who were converted to Catholicism mainly in the first half of the twentieth century – and of some who didn't quite make it. Starting with Oscar Wilde – on whom Pearce has written a splendid new biography – he covers the lot, right through to Muggeridge and G.M. Brown, and includes such Catholic manqués as T.S.Eliot and C.S.Lewis. From any point of view it was an extraordinary process. Pearce brings out the way these people's minds worked and how they influenced each other, and also gives an accurate picture of the anti-Catholic prejudice at all levels which formed part of the background to their decisions. A fascinating study of the leading literary lights of the 20th Century who became Catholics. **(P)**

16. Mother Angelica, by Raymond Arroyo (2005, Doubleday). When the history of the Church in the 20th Century comes to be written, an important figure in the story of evangelisation will certainly be Mother Angelica. A simple Franciscan nun, born of Italian parents in 1923, she would hardly be the obvious choice to found the most influential Catholic TV network in the world. Her story, and that of E.W.T.N. has been brilliantly researched and written by one of the network's best presenters.

17. My Name Escapes Me, by Alec Guinness (1997, Penguin; biography). Guinness was one of the finest English actors of the last century and a convert to Catholicism. This is the last of his diaries and autobiographical writings. Guinness combines shrewd and at times mordant observation of the glittering world in which he lived with an awareness of his own faults and his need for religious sustenance.

18. Not the Whole Truth, by John Cardinal Heenan (1971, Hodder and Stoughton). An immensely readable account of a priest's life – a priest who would in due course become an Archbishop and a Cardinal. From a secret trip to Stalin's Russia – his descriptions of the atmosphere of fear in Moscow are chilling – to accounts of rescue work in the London Blitz, this autobiography of Cardinal Heenan is a fascinating read. Well-grounded faith, self-discipline, realism and common sense ring through the pages. **(P)**

19. Orthodoxy, by G. K. Chesterton * (First published 1908; 1995, 2006 Ignatius Press; apologetics/autobiography). The companion (and sequel) to *Heretics*, *Orthodoxy* sees Chesterton set out his own beliefs, which are the tenets of orthodox Christianity and ultimately (as Chesterton realized) find their full expression only in the Catholic Church. The book is, in the author's own words, 'unavoidably affirmative and therefore unavoidably autobiographical'. Chesterton describes his own personal escape from 'the suicide of thought' represented by modern philosophies of life and, to his own great surprise, his discovery of truth, happiness and beauty in the Christian faith. An unconventional approach to Christian dogma, but a very powerful one. He embarks on an intellectual quest, and his common sense shows him that the Christian view of the world is the most sensible and the most exciting. You'll probably find yourself marking passages on almost every page to quote or re-read. Chesterton was a major influence on several generations of Christian converts, who found in him the intelligence, wisdom, and wit that makes faith fun as well as serious. Chesterton has the ability to make us see things anew. Follow up with *The Catholic Church and Conversion*, or *The Everlasting Man*, or *The Well and the Shallows*, or almost any book by this profound but unfailingly entertaining writer. Gilbert K. Chesterton explains how and why he came to believe in Christianity.

20. Seven Storey Mountain, by Thomas Merton (1946; 1999, SPCK; autobiography). Merton's fascinating and honest account of his own struggle towards faith, after a childhood exposed to a variety of influences and cultures, and an adolescence in which he firmly rejected God. Gradually, he recognizes the presence of truth in the Catholic Church, and aged 23 is formally received. Merton wrote this biography aged 31, having been a Cistercian monk for 5 years. His journey has deep resonances with the problems facing contemporary youth, and his intelligence and clarity make for a compelling book that will find echoes within the readers' own experience.

21. Something Beautiful for God: Mother Teresa of Calcutta, by Malcolm Muggeridge (1997, HarperCollins; biography). An early biography that brought Mother Teresa to the attention of the world. This is still one of the best introductions to the life and work of Mother Teresa, written by a British journalist who was unexpectedly captivated by the love that radiated from this extraordinary woman. It captures not just the spirit of this great woman, but also the bewilderment and joy of the author as he slowly begins to understand her. Well illustrated.

22. Story of a Soul, by St Thérèse of Lisieux (Various editions; autobiography). Also entitled *Autobiography of a Saint*. The 'Little Flower' is one of the most popular and influential saints of our times. Her immense popularity is largely based upon this book. It is her own personal testimony, written at odd moments in school exercise books and on scraps of paper. It gives a vivid account of the life of a saint from the inside; intimate, spontaneous, and sparkling with humour. She is not at all the sugary and sentimental saint that some people imagine. Her spirituality is a distillation of the Scriptures and the Carmelite masters; and her truthfulness and steely intelligence shine through her writing.

23. The Curé d'Ars, St Jean-Marie-Baptiste Vianney, by Abbé Francis Trochu (2007, Tan Books; biography). This is the best biography of the Curé d'Ars, and probably one of the best saints' lives ever. It gives full details of the incredible life of the saint, who resembled the Desert Fathers in his austerity, and was one of the great positive influences on Church life in the 19th Century. Yet, St John Vianney could also be very amusing and the book is enlivened by anecdotes about his activities. In particular, though, it brings home the tremendous importance of the sacrament of confession in living a truly Catholic life. **(P)**

24. The Heart Must Break, by James Maudsley (2001, Century; autobiography). This adventure story becomes a devastating indictment of the Burmese Junta. Maudsley was a young Englishman sentenced to 17 years in prison after chaining himself to the railings in Rangoon, to draw the world's attention to the genocide against the Karen people. Through his physical and mental battles with his guards, he proves his determination not to allow his spirit to be crushed by oppressors. Maudsley's painfully truthful attempts to put on record his worst aspects only serve to make this fine character shine more brightly.

25. The Hunted Priest, by John Gerard * (1959, Fontana; autobiography / history). John Gerard's extraordinary memoir of life as a missionary Jesuit priest in Elizabethan England paints a terrifying picture of life in the Catholic underground from the perspective of a man who escaped the bloody fate of so many of his brother-priests to tell the tale. A friend of the poet St Robert Southwell, John Gerard ministered to the recusant population before being arrested, imprisoned and subjected to horrific 'wall torture' that left him maimed for life. The matter-of-fact narration of his clandestine landing, his evasion of capture as he served the underground Church, his meetings with future martyrs, and his eventual arrest, interrogation, and torture in the Tower of London bring those times back to vivid life. His audacious escape from the Tower of London is the stuff of epic adventures and offers a fascinating glimpse into a much-neglected part of England's heritage. The perfect antidote to *Elizabeth: The Golden Age*.

26. The Long Loneliness, by Dorothy Day * (1952, 1996, Harper San Francisco; autobiography). Dorothy Day lived an extraordinary life. Born in Chicago, she became a radical political journalist in New York, living a bohemian and largely godless life. Love and motherhood brought her to faith, and eventually to the Catholic Church. She tried to combine her commitment to the poor and to a just social order with her Christian faith. With the help of Peter Maurin she founded the Catholic Worker Movement in the 1930s, setting up a newspaper, opening Houses of Hospitality in the cities and farms in the countryside. This movement transformed the American Church's commitment to social justice, and brought thousands of Catholics to become more involved in work for peace, and in an active love for the poor and the marginalized through the practice of the Works of Mercy. Her humanity, passion, humour and sensitivity shine through this beautiful autobiography. Though often in trouble with the Church's leadership during her lifetime, she has come to be widely recognized as a saint. Pope John Paul II granted the Archdiocese of New York permission to open Dorothy Day's "cause" in March 2000.

27. The Monks of Tibhirine: Faith, love and terror in Algeria, by John W. Kiser (2002, St Martin's Press). Informative and inspiring, but very harrowing in parts, this book describes the lives of the small community of Trappist monks at the monastery of Tibhirine in Algeria before and after the country fell prey to extremist terrorists, following the cancelled elections of 1992. The book provides a detailed background of the eventful story of Algeria. The monks established strong friendships with their local Muslim neighbours and kept up their religious life with enormous faith and determination. Finally, in 1996, seven of them were kidnapped and murdered.

28. The Path to Rome, by Hilaire Belloc (1902; 2005, Dover Publications). The delightful and high-spirited account of Belloc's pilgrimage from Toul, in France, to Rome. The account focuses on the countryside through which Belloc walks, but also reveals much of Belloc himself, his own spiritual journey, and indeed his yearning for company. The young author vows to travel on foot, by the most direct route, hearing Mass every morning – all of which vows are eventually broken. But shining through is his optimism, his humorous observation of the countryside that he sees, and above all, his deep and lively faith.

Fiction

29. A Boy in the Gulag, by Jerzy Kmiecik (1983, Quartet Books, London and New York). For an understanding of the grim reality of life in a Soviet labour camp, the horror of Stalin's Russia, and the misery brought to Eastern Europe by Communism, read this book. Better still, pass it on to one of those tiresome people who, living comfortably in the West during the worst years of Communist rule in the USSR, murmur cosily about how Marxism is really rather a good system and that the labour camps were probably necessary for certain groups of people and did no real harm.

30. Brighton Rock, by Graham Greene (1991, Penguin). Although Greene would describe *Brighton Rock* as an 'entertainment' rather than a serious novel, it offers plenty of opportunities to reflect on issues of justice and conscience. The book skillfully intertwines an evocative account of life in the seedy underworld of 1930s Brighton with the thrilling tale of a woman's pursuit of justice. While the childhood Catholicism of the novel's villainous anti-hero is hardly a good advertisement for the Christian life, Greene confronts his readers with the essential questions of mercy and redemption.

31. Brideshead Revisited, by Evelyn Waugh * (1945; 1981, Penguin Books; fiction). Charles Ryder, a student at Oxford, encounters Sebastian Flyte, and through him becomes drawn into the life of the aristocratic Flyte family at their ancestral home, Brideshead. As an agnostic observer, Charles is mesmerized by the deeply-rooted Catholicism of the family; his eventual romantic attachment to Lady Julia Flyte is doomed by her loyalty to Catholic values. In later life, Charles finds himself returning to a now empty Brideshead, and relives many of the emotions that he experienced there. Waugh avowedly wrote his greatest novel as a meditation upon grace working within the frailty and folly of the human heart.

32. Death Comes for the Archbishop, by Willa Cather (1927, Virago Modern Classics; fiction). If you want a good understanding of the obstacles the Church faced in establishing herself as a loving institution in the world, not of it, you will find no better account than this one. It begins: "One summer evening in the year 1848 three Cardinals and a missionary Bishop from America were dining together in the garden of a villa in the Sabine hills, overlooking Rome." Based on the true story of a Bishop and his colleague who are sent by Rome to New Mexico in the 19th Century to reawaken the Catholic faith, Cather – not a Catholic – sympathetically and hauntingly captures the aching slog of evangelisation in alien and unforgiving territory.

33. Fabiola: A tale of the catacombs, by Cardinal Nicholas Wiseman (1997, Lepanto Press; fiction). A classic historical novel set in 4th Century Rome. This is the age of the early church martyrs and Cardinal Wiseman, himself a classical scholar, gives us a glimpse into the world of Diocletian and the last and fiercest persecution of Roman Christians. Both fictional and historical characters intermingle in this hugely edifying story of faith and charity. In the story and we learn a great deal about the life of Christians 'in the catacombs'. The primary heroine is Fabiola who becomes a Christian through the examples of her devoted slave Syra and the fearless acceptance of martyrdom by the early Christians. It is a story of with many twists and turns and the characters are very vivid and richly imagined. We meet flesh and blood representations of St Pancratius, St Sebastian and St Agnes. Fabiola is treasure for those who enjoy Rome and its antiquities and especially for those with a love of Patristics.

34. Father Elijah – An Apocalypse, by Michael D O'Brien * (1996, Ignatius Press; fiction). This novel forms the climax of O'Brien's six-part series, *Children of the Last Days*. It tells the story of a Carmelite friar called from obscurity by the Vatican to try to turn the European President from the path of disaster. O'Brien provides an unrivalled insight into the struggles playing themselves out in our own days, and a veritable handbook of how to stand against evil. It is the kind of book you will feel drawn back to again and again. O'Brien's stark and prophetic indictment of our culture has the pace, sense of threat, and excitement of a thriller. His depiction of the disobedience rampant amongst members of the Church is sadly accurate and shocking. The unexpected climax of the novel is unforgettable. This is a Catholic Apocalypse, a monumental novel, with nuggets of wisdom and thought-provoking insights on every page. It shows how faith and humility can transform a broken life; and how the beauty of Christ sheds light on the most difficult situations. Gives a revealing picture of how spiritual forces – good and evil – are at work in the world, and how God's Providence is working in events and in the lives of his people.

35. In This House of Brede, by Rumer Godden (1991, Pan Paperback; fiction). Rumer Godden based her novel on the Benedictine Abbey that was at Stanbrook, which she grew to know well. In the Introduction she quotes Dame Felicitas Corrigan as saying that she wished 'that someone would write a book about nuns as they really are, not as the author wants them to be'. Godden succeeds admirably, writing a book that is true to life, warts and all, and yet at the same time has a serenity and integrity and warmth that is always present in religious life, underneath it all. A beautiful read.

36. Katherine, by Anya Seton (1954, Hodder; fiction). A historical novel based on the life of a real character, Katherine, who eventually married John of Gaunt and became the forebear of kings. This meticulously researched story is based on actual characters and gives a fascinating insight into England in the 14th Century and into Catholic life which was taken for granted at that time. Katherine's difficulties and those of her children are brought into focus in the light of Catholic society and culture, giving a glimpse of how the English Church might have developed its spirituality by drawing on the insights of its mystics such as Julian of Norwich, had it not been for the Reformation and the more severe approach this necessitated.

37. Kristen Lavrensdatter, by Sigrid Undset (1997, Penguin US; fiction). One of the great novels of the 20th Century by a Norwegian Catholic, this is an epic work of great persuasiveness and power, set in mediaeval Scandinavia. It is a long and immensely satisfying work. As well as setting out for us a detailed and compelling account of a truly Catholic culture, this is an account of the life of a young girl, growing through womanhood and marriage, until old age, with beautifully drawn and moving depictions of the relationship between the young Kristen and her parents; between Kristen and her lover and then husband; and finally between Kristen and her many children.

38. Lord of the World, by Robert Hugh Benson * (1908; 2001, St Augustine's Press; 2005, Once and Future Books; fiction). Msgr. Hugh Benson, the youngest son of E.W. Benson, Archbishop of Canterbury, scandalised the Anglican establishment by converting to Catholicism in 1903. Though a towering literary figure in his day, he is now largely, but undeservedly, forgotten. *Lord of the World*, written in 1907, stands beside Huxley's *Brave New World* and Orwell's *Nineteen Eighty-Four* as a futuristic, dystopian, fantasy. This story about the rise of the Antichrist, Armageddon, and the Second Coming of Christ, reads like an account of our near future. Set in London, Surrey, Rome, and Israel, Benson describes a world where a triumphant secularism barely tolerates the co-existence of the Church in society. This is a world made in man's image, where euthanasia masquerades as mercy, and a pervasive sceptical humanism leads to wide-spread apostasy. But this is merely the prelude to the advent of the Antichrist, who leads the final war against the Church. Benson's uncanny depiction of our times from 100 years ago, gives this novel the feeling of prophecy. What comes as a surprise is the action of God's providence which even amidst the greatest human darkness brings about the ultimate triumph of Christ. This apocalyptic novel is set in a future where religion has been abandoned or suppressed, with the Catholic Church the only remaining spiritual force. Benson vividly depicts a world where Churches are closed and Catholicism survives only in enclaves, while humanist and atheist values are raised up above those of God. The resulting conflict brings about the apocalypse, and the final revelation of God. Benson's novel gives a fascinating glimpse of the preoccupations and outlook of English Catholics in the age of Chesterton and Belloc.

39. The Big Fisherman, by Lloyd C. Douglas (1965, Pan Books; fiction). Set in the Eastern Mediterranean and Palestine of the first century, Fara seeks revenge against her father, Herod Antipas, who humiliated and deserted her mother. Journeying to Galilee, Fara is befriended by Peter, the Big Fisherman, and drawn into the events of Jesus' life, death, and resurrection. This retelling of the life of Jesus and the apostles is one of the most moving because of its faithfulness to the Church's understanding about the person of Christ, and the novel's focus on St Peter's emotional and spiritual journey to become the rock on which the Church is founded.

40. The Bridge of San Luis Rey, by Thornton Wilder * (1927; 2000, Penguin Classics; fiction). This is a classic novel about God's Providence. The story takes place in Peru in 1714, when Peru was under Spanish colonial rule. The bridge of San Luis Rey over a deep gorge collapses, and five people are killed. Brother Juniper witnessed the accident, and tries to reason why these particular five people died in the accident. In doing so, he recreates the lives of these people who come from different walks of society. The novel raises questions of life, death, suffering, unhappiness, love, and belief in God as opposed to chance. It also describes the hypocrisy, vanity and intricacies of Peruvian society of the times. Brother Juniper, in his experiment of trying to understand and discover the mind of

God through reason, in fact discovers through his examination of the lives of these complex characters that the mind of God far surpasses his original aim of justifying the ways of God to man. The accident is a catalyst in revealing the great mystery of God which is beyond man's comprehension. The ways of God are mysterious, but never without meaning, purpose and love: was this a waste of human life, demonstrating that we are no more than flies and 'sport for the gods', or can we still discern the hand of the God of love?

41. The Chosen, by Chaim Potok (1973, Penguin). Set in wartime New York this story follows the friendship of the two sons of two very different rabbis thrown together by a baseball accident. One is the son of a Tzaddik (a hereditary rabbi) from the Hassidic tradition, hermetically sealed from the outside world, and the other is the son of a forward thinking Zionist liberal rabbi. The powerful clash of faith and tradition in a fast-changing world resonate with many of the struggles inside the Church today. And the eternal themes of fathers and sons, and human suffering are beautifully explored. The whole is interspersed with wonderful insights into Jewish piety and study of scripture and tradition which will inspire all to a greater love of the Word of God.

42. The Clowns of God, by Morris West (1981, Hodder and Stoughton; fiction). Set in the future, Pope Gregory XVII is forced to abdicate by the Curia because of his determination to publish an encyclical exhorting the Church and humanity to prepare for the end of the world and the Second Coming of Christ, based on his claim of a private revelation. Set against the very real fears of a nuclear war that were current in the

1980s, the novel is a gripping exploration of faith, the politics of global conflict, and terrorism. This is one of the best examples of Morris West's forte – the evocation of the power of love, and the courage to believe in the face of doubt and the enormity of evil.

43. The Devil's Advocate, by Morris West (1959, Coronet Books, Hodder and Stoughton; fiction). Set in poverty stricken, post-war Italy, a terminally ill Vatican official sets off to a backwater village, given the job of finding out if Giacomo Nerone, a mysterious visitor who was executed during the German retreat, should be considered for canonisation as a saint. A wonderful exploration of what gives life its meaning, and of the power of love, through a range of fascinating and flawed characters, all of whom knew Nerone, and who have burning questions for the Church - and God himself - to answer.

44. The Father Brown Stories, by G.K. Chesterton (2005, Ignatius hardback; Penguin, selected). As with C.S.Lewis, any of Chesterton's works could have been chosen, but the Father Brown stories are as good an entry into Chesterton's Catholic world as any. I read them as our set book at the age of 12 at Grammar school, and it set me on the road to the Catholic Church. In his book *Orthodoxy* the abiding insight was that of 'paradox'. The Catholic Church's teaching is truly catholic, embracing seemingly paradoxical affirmations into a genuine synthesis, whereas Protestant thought tends to pick one side to the exclusion of the other.

45. The Gulag Archipelago, by Alexander Solzenhitsyn (1973, Harvill Press). A most important book of the 20th Century, it documents the huge and ghastly network of human misery in the bitter cold, filth, torture and disease of the labour camps of the Soviet Union. Here, men suffered starvation and sickness, exhaustion and vicious cruelty – and the author knew of their experiences because he was one of them, sentenced to hard labour in a camp beyond the Arctic Circle for criticising Stalin's rule in the 1940s. It's important to know how all this happened, and learn what a godless and evil government can do to its people.

46. The Happiness of Father Happe, by Cecily Hallack (1946, Brown and Nolan). *Father Happe* is the gentle story of a new priest's arrival in an ordinary English parish. Avoiding the spectacular, it explores how his exuberance and concentration on Christ's message touches the everyday lives of the people he meets, Catholic and non-Catholic alike. This is not an account of the transformation of people's lives through the intervention of extraordinary power but a believable attempt to find hope and courage - to find Jesus - in all aspects of life's challenges, richness, health, illness and suffering. A book which makes you long to emulate a total trust in Jesus.

47. The Lord of the Rings, by J.R.R. Tolkien (1960, George Allen & Unwin; fiction). Almost too obvious to mention, although many people don't realize how Catholic it is in spirit, this epic fantasy novel by an Oxford don (a sequel to his children's story, *The Hobbit*), is rightly one of the most popular books of all time. Imbued with a profound sense of providence and grace, the beauty of virtue and the loveliness of the natural world, it explores the nature of temptation and the struggle against evil in the human heart. We emerge refreshed and invigorated. Read it every few years, and follow up with *The Children of Hurin*, *The Silmarillion* or *The Letters of J.R.R. Tolkien*.

48. The Painted Veil, by William Somerset Maugham (2006, Vintage Books, fiction). Somerset Maugham is fascinated with Catholicism in many of his novels and writes about it with understanding and appreciation. This novel, based on an event recorded by Dante, tells of a doctor who takes his straying wife to a city infected by plague. This punishment becomes redemptive for her, for their marriage, and for the doctor himself. An important element in this outcome is the community of French sisters who work with the children and plague victims of the place. Their alternative lifestyle, and the love that motivates it, help the couple to journey from anger and disharmony to compassion and reconciliation.

49. The Power and the Glory, by Graham Greene * (1940; 1969, Penguin; 2001, Vintage; fiction). Based on his travels to the southern Mexican states of Jalisco and Chiapas in early 1938 and set in 1930s Mexico during an anti-clerical purge, Greene's masterpiece follows the story of a whiskey-priest fleeing a martyrdom he will eventually be called to face. Though at times cowardly and weak, the priest is constantly aware of his failings - which include alcoholism and a child fathered during an affair with his housekeeper - and seemingly unaware that his journey through the squalor of shanty towns and prisons is leading him towards sainthood. This is a book for anyone who has ever despaired of God's mercy and the eventual triumph of the Church. The description of perfect contrition at the end must surely be one of the most moving pieces of prose writing penned in the 20th Century. A sublime depiction of grace working through fallen human beings, and the ability of the Church to survive even against desperate odds, this book needs to be set reading for every seminarian. A picture of God's grace working in the rawness of humanity. Marvellous insights into human nature – all the major and minor characters are richly drawn. And a tense thriller too.

50. The Red Horse, by Eugenio Corti (2005, Ignatius Press; fiction). Epic novel set in Italy during the traumatic events of the Second World War and its aftermath, exploring the effects of politics and war on ordinary lives. A story of love, marriage, community and everyday life in a Catholic country; and of incredible, truly hellish suffering (such as the retreat from Russia and the prisoner-of-war camps) which gives a human dimension to the all-too-easily-forgotten horrors of the 20th Century, including the destructive ideology of communism. Yet, the light of a supernatural faith brings hope and resolution, most powerfully when we follow the journey of the characters' souls after death.

51. The Stories of J.F. Powers, by J.F. Powers (2008, New York; fiction). An anthology of the short stories of J. F. Powers (1917 -1999), a writer whose affectionate and telling satires of parish life in small-town middle-America in the 1950s remain completely fresh. Powers and Flannery O'Connor (*see below*) are two completely different writers in terms of content and register – but each, in their own way, is completely catholic.

52. The White Witch, by Elizabeth Goudge (1958, Hodder, fiction). Set at the start of the English Civil War, this story follows the fortunes of a divided family and explores the themes of loyalty and conflict, good and evil within the framework of war and religious division. The fate of a Jesuit priest is bound up with the family and his struggle with loyalty and faith is sensitively handled.

53. Wise Blood, by Flannery O'Connor (2007, Farrer Straus; fiction). This short novel captures the essence of an age of unbelief: The Church of Jesus Christ without Jesus Christ. (Allegorical for Catholics as: The Church without the Blessed Sacrament). Hazel Motes, the anti-hero, is a young, angry man intent on a life without hypocrisy. His passion for truth challenges Protestant culture. V.S. Pritchett writes the introduction to this remarkable story that will leave you wondering and reeling about life, liberty and the pursuit of God. He writes: "Flannery O'Connor is a master of the fear and obsession and of the images that haunt ignorant minds...[she] has the art of making the preposterous appear to be natural to her people."

54. World of Don Camillo, by Giovanni Guareschi (1980, Gollancz; fiction). Set in the Po Valley, Italy, during the 1950s, this is a collection of humorous episodes about the rivalry, practical jokes, and friendship between the irascible parish priest, Don Camilo, and the provocative communist mayor, Peponne. What makes Guareschi's humour delightful is his characterisation of the intimate relationship between Don Camilo and Jesus, who advises, admonishes, and encourages the priest from the Crucifix in the Church. These are very touching stories because of Guareschi's love for his characters, and an Italy that has gone. **(P)**

History

55. A History of the Crusades, by Steven Runciman (1987, Cambridge University Press, Vols I, II, & III). Prof Runciman is a superb history writer with a vast range of knowledge of medieval Europe and its impact on the middle Eastern world in particular. He tells the stories of the Crusades with great care and detail, seeking genuinely to understand why they took place and what they were for. His accounts are vivid, in some instances quite humorous and in others sadly poignant. These books are a really terrific read, especially, but not only, for those who love history. And they are hugely significant today when relations between the countries involved, as well as the three great traditions of faith that thrive here (Judaism, Christianity and Islam) seem to be more tense and troubled than ever. Readers may develop a deeper awareness of the forces that shape these relationships and appreciate why so many of the problems we currently face resist easy resolution.

56. God's Secret Agents: Queen Elizabeth's forbidden priests, by Alice Hogge (2006, Harper; history). Hogge tells with considerable skill the intricate story of the priests who laboured in secret to keep the Catholic Faith alive in the years following the defeat of the Spanish Armada, and of the machinations of the Elizabethan and Jacobean state to defeat them. It is clear that the Jesuits sought no political solution, but the actions of the Gunpowder Plotters were to prove disastrous for them, and were used by the Government to portray all Catholics as traitors. This is a wonderful and lucid account of the situation of Catholicism in Elizabethan England, and of the true causes and consequences of the Gunpowder Plot.

57. Hiroshima, by John Hersey (1946, Penguin; history). This is a celebrated account by an American war correspondent of the sufferings experienced by the inhabitants of Hiroshima after the dropping of the first atomic bomb on 6 August 1945. Among those Hersey interviewed for his account were survivors of the Jesuit community in the city. When it was first published in the *New Yorker* this account did more than anything else to make people aware of the terrible effects of the dropping of the bomb, in unemotional and calm prose.

58. Shadowplay, by Clare Asquith * (2005, Public Affairs, New York; non-fiction). Much has been written recently on Shakespeare's Catholicism, and to what degree he was a recusant. This is an unusual internal examination of all his main plays, in which Lady Asquith has identified a hidden code, criticising the Elizabethan regime. Indeed, reading his sonnets in the light of his Catholic faith seems to be the key to understanding them. Clare Asquith's book is an in-depth study of his plays in their historical context, plotting the hopes and bitter disappointments of Catholics as they came under increasing persecution. It gives intelligent insight, not only into Shakespeare's plays but into the Catholic situation of the time, sometimes almost unbearably poignant. The idea came from seeing plays in Moscow, before the iron curtain fell, which also contained hidden codes. Much more exciting and scholarly than the *Da Vinci* nonsense.

59. The Blood and the Shroud, by Ian Wilson (1998, Weidenfeld & Nicolson; history). Ian Wilson, a historian, examines the evidence for and against the Shroud of Turin being the genuine burial cloth of Jesus in the light of the 1988 controversial carbon dating test. Wilson makes a convincing case for the scientific and historical basis for still maintaining that the Turin Shroud preserves the actual image of Jesus' body, bearing the marks of his passion and death. Looking at the Turin Shroud with the eyes of faith, with the credibility of its historical origins restored, is a truly moving act of devotion.

60. The Crisis of Civilization, by Hilaire Belloc (1992, Tan Books; Church History). This book demonstrates how the Protestant Reformation was the great watershed in the progressive destruction of Christendom, and thus how it led to the present crisis which our Civilization is in. Belloc focuses on the economic effects of the Reformation, and how they led to the creation of the modern world. He saw the only remedy for the world in a return to authentic Catholicism, and this book corrects the distorted view which saw the Reformation only in positive terms.

61. The Passion and Martyrdom of the Holy English Carthusian Fathers: A short narrative, by Maurice Chauncey (1935, SPCK London; history). The extraordinary first-hand description (originally written in Latin) of the last days of the London Charterhouse and the martyrdom of 18 of the Carthusian monks, including the Prior John Houghton. What is unique to this gripping history is that Chauncey was himself part of the events, being at the time a young monk at the monastery. He eventually took the Oath of Supremacy, but was haunted by his betrayal, and later wrote this book partly as an expiation of his failure. A moving and priceless portrayal of the end of Catholic England, and the heroic witness of the Henrican martyrs. **(P)**

62. The Six Wives of Henry VIII, by Alison Weir (1992, Pimlico; history). Chilling and thrilling with lots of killing. Learn how it was the Protestant, Anne of Cleves, rejected by Henry for lack of beauty, who is the real heroine of this true Tudor tale. She ends her days with her head still on her shoulders, rich, landed, Anglicised and converted to the true Faith: Catholicism! Another insight gleaned from this excellent account of an old story, is that Henry was reading *The Prince* by Machievelli, which may explain the disaster this Catholic King fell into - had he not bought into the idea that there is no distinction between a good King and a Tyrant, we'd still be in Merry Old England and not today's Britain; and, it wasn't all Protestant theology's fault. Blame a Florentine!

63. The Stripping of the Altars: Traditional religion in England 1400-1580, by Eamon Duffy * (1992, 2005, 2nd Ed., Yale University Press; history). The book that changed for ever our view of the Reformation, revealing that the late medieval Church was vibrant and popular, and that the 16th Century changes in religion were not an inevitable outcome of a failed system. Duffy firstly gives a fascinating and detailed description of the Catholic life of England on the eve of the Reformation, and then recounts the religious changes – mostly deeply unpopular – that destroyed a thousand years of tradition. It is a painful book for Catholics to read, but essential for a true understanding of the religious history of our country. A seminal work on pre-Reformation England, which is already causing other historians to revise their stance on the Reformation, and also books by Scott Hahn, especially *The Lamb's Supper* on the Mass, and *Hail Holy Queen*, on Our Lady, which give understanding of the Catholic, Biblical teaching on these two topics, helpful to Catholic and non-Catholic alike. A now classic description of the Reformation and its impact as experienced in the ordinary parishes of England by one of the world's leading church historians. Prof. Duffy writes so clearly and sympathetically of this crucial time in the history of the Church, giving many photographic illustrations and descriptions of places to visit in order to see for oneself what took place here. A superb exploration of a difficult and still sensitive subject, and one that can make us more aware of many of the issues the Church is facing today.

Spiritual reading

64. Abandonment to Divine Providence, by Jean-Pierre de Caussade (1975, Image Books Doubleday, trans. John Beeversm; spirituality). Based on advice given in the early 18th Century by a French Jesuit priest to the nuns at Nancy, collected together more than a hundred years after his death, this classic bears comparison with *The Story of a Soul* by St Therese, or *Introduction to the Devout Life* by St Francis de Sales. Chosen because it is slightly less well known, because it is tiny and because it has a lovely, direct and simple way of everyday holiness, the "sacrament of the present moment", about which it speaks so clearly and intensely.

65. Blessed Elizabeth of the Trinity: The works (1995, ICS, 2 Vols pub to date; spirituality). Blessed Elizabeth of the Trinity (Elizabeth Catez) was a contemporary of Saint Therese of Lisieux, entering Carmel at the age of 21 in 1901, and dying at the age of 26. She is becoming increasingly well known as one of the greatest mystics of the 20th Century, and especially through her *'Prayer to the Trinity'* which is quoted in the *Catechism of the Catholic Church.* Called an 'apostle of the Holy Spirit' her emphasis was on the indwelling of the Blessed Trinity, living here and now the vocation of a 'Praise of Glory' that would be fulfilled in heaven.

66. Brave New Family: Selected articles, by G.K. Chesterton (1992, Ignatius; non-fiction). This anthology of Chesterton's writings on the family, marriage, childhood and human sexuality offers an excellent introduction to both Chesterton's work and the Church's teachings. Provocative, witty and devastatingly prophetic, Chesterton's writings defending the Church's teachings make an enjoyable and illuminating read for a generation who have grown up in the world Chesterton predicted would come to pass.

67. Christendom Awake: On re-energizing the Church in culture, by Aidan Nichols OP (1999, Eerdmans). A lively and enthusiastic call for attention to the intellectual and spiritual needs of the contemporary world. Fr Aidan writes energetically about the crisis of culture which will be recognisably familiar to most Catholics, and suggests ways in which the Church might once again and become a shaping force in the world. Topics include many things that appear repeatedly in the media, which can so easily leave us muttering in disgust at what is happening in the world today. This book doesn't let us get away with that, but challenges us to understand these problems more deeply and to enter into them confidently as people of faith.

68. Faith of our Fathers: Reflections on Catholic traditions, by Eamon Duffy (2006, Continuum). A most thoughtful reflection on traditional Catholic prayer and practices which are precious gifts of the tradition to contemporary believers. Descriptions of the veneration of saints, prayers for the dead, devotion to Our Lady, and others, many of which come up as subjects in ecumenical debate, are here lovingly described and with great joy in their continued expression. Every Catholic would do well to understand more deeply what these things mean in their own devotions and learn how to explain them to other people who may ask what they're all about. In this way, the book serves as a good resource for evangelisation.

69. Fatima in Lucia's Own Words, by Sr Lucia (2000, Postulation Centre, Fatima; ed. by Fr Louis Kondor; spirituality). This is definitely the best book on Fatima. It contains the four memoirs written by Sr Lucia at the request of the original bishop of Fatima. She focuses particularly on the lives of her fellow seers Jacinta and Francisco, and makes it easy to understand why they were declared Blesseds recently, and will no doubt be canonised in due course. Sr Lucia also shows that the real message of Fatima is about allowing Our Lady complete freedom to lead us to God, while also emphasising the importance of the rosary and the Five First Saturdays devotion.

70. Four Witnesses, by Rod Bennett (1997, Ignatius Press; non-fiction). There is an increasing interest in the Early Church Fathers, and this book is a superb introduction, not only into their writings, but into their world. Rod Bennett deals with Clement of Rome, Ignatius of Antioch, Justin Martyr, Irenaeus of Lyons, quoting extensively from their writings and putting them into their historical context as the Church leaves the time of the Apostles into the uncharted waters of the post-Apostolic Age – would the Holy Spirit still be with them to guide them?

71. Introduction to the Devout Life, by St Francis de Sales *
(1609, first published as *Introduction à la Vie Devoté*; 1962, Burns and Oates; 2007, Cosimo; prayer/spirituality). St Francis' book is an excellent first port of call for anyone wishing to deepen their spiritual life. Honest, practical and above all, gently and sensitively written, this is as close a reader can come to being given personal spiritual direction by a saint and Doctor of the Church. 'Would that this book were in the hands of all',

wrote Pope Pius XI. St Francis de Sales' simple introduction to the spiritual life, written for the use of laypeople living busy lives in the 'ordinary world' is certainly one of the all-time spiritual classics, and deserves a place on the bookshelves of anyone seriously trying to develop a life of prayer. Written with St Francis' famous gentleness and sweetness, yet not afraid to be ruthlessly challenging when necessary, this book will introduce you to simple methods of mental prayer, gives material for meditation, offers sage advice on the common obstacles awaiting those beginning to live the spiritual life, and above all, will guide you, as it promises, to a more generous love of God and your neighbour. This a work by a saint about how to become a saint. The secret of the devout and holy life is not found in doing great and heroic deeds but in performing our particular vocations with love, care and attention. This is the meaning of devotion. St Francis de Sales gives great encouragement to all that holiness can be achieved in the very simple and practical ways of everyday life. This is a spiritual gem which teaches the beginner in the spiritual life the basics of prayer and the ways of virtue. This is a book which can be read again and again, and is really a complete guide to the spiritual life for anyone living in the world. It is certainly a spiritual classic well worth buying and reading. No need to read it from start to finish: Dip into the chapters that seem useful.

72. Leisure: the basis of culture, by Josef Pieper * (1965, Collins / Fontana; 1998, St. Augustine's Press; trans. Gerald Malsbary; philosophy). The eminent German Catholic philosopher preferred to publish short books and essays. If you want to tell the Protestant Work Ethic to take a break, read this book. Do not read its 150 pages quickly. Do it leisurely, by the pool, sipping a cool drink and applying another layer of sun-tan oil. While all those busybodies work themselves to the bone, you will unwind and see that Time is not Money but something far more valuable and expensive: its point is doing just what you are doing; thinking just what you are thinking; and Pieper enables you to do this with value. When you go back to work, you will be wiser and more grateful and, sadly, probably more productive: *but that wasn't the point of reading the book!*

73. Letters from the Desert, by Carlo Carretto (1972; 2002, Darton, Longman and Todd). Following in the footsteps of Charles de Foucauld, Carretto withdrew from his active life to become a desert contemplative. This short book is packed with his deep, meditative thoughts on many subjects. In his words it was "...matured in solitude and took shape around an activity, which has been, without any doubt, the greatest gift that the Sahara has given me: prayer." His allegory is that the desert is found everywhere in our daily lives, and the challenge of the Gospel is to make an oasis of love in whatever desert we live. An ideal book to gently mull over on a retreat.

74. Loving the Church, by Cardinal Christoph Schonborn (1998, Ignatius Press; spiritual reading). Cardinal Schonborn, now Archbishop of Vienna and general editor of the *Catechism of the Catholic Church*, originally preached this series of powerful meditations in the presence of Pope John Paul II and the Papal Household during the Lenten retreat of 1996. As the title implies, all the meditations have the Church as their theme, and develop into a comprehensive and beautiful study of the Mystical Body of Christ. A valuable corrective to those who would see the Church purely in 'institutional' terms, this would also be excellent spiritual reading for anyone preparing for reception into the Church, or thinking of doing so.

75. Parochial and Plain Sermons, by John Henry Newman (1987, Ignatius Press; homiletics). Collected into one volume of over 1700 pages on bible-thin paper, this book contains years of spiritual reading. The spirit as well as the theology of Newman is in these sermons, and although they were delivered as an Anglican he saw no need to suppress them or make changes after he went over to Rome. Newman's influence continues to grow, and this would be a good way of getting to know him better. There is a companion volume of *Prayers, Verses and Devotions.* **(P)**

76. The Four Cardinal Virtues, by Josef Pieper (1964, University of Notre Dame Press; philosophy). Drawing on the wisdom of Plato and Aristotle, and re-thinking Aquinas in view of the questions posed by Kant, Pieper here offers four essays on prudence, justice, fortitude and temperance. But that background should not put the reader off: Pieper is a masterly teacher and his writing is always direct and lively, free of technical jargon. In the case of each virtue he summarises admirably what the great tradition has to say about it and shows how it engages the whole human being, from the most physical to the most spiritual level. **(P)**

77. The Great Divorce: A dream, by CS Lewis * (1977, Fount Paperbacks; fiction). Lewis' very English portrayal of the Four Last things – death, judgement, Heaven and Hell – begins with the protagonist standing in a bus queue, unknowingly waiting for a bus that will take him to purgatory. Lewis' genius for looking at familiar Christian doctrines in new ways, such as sin, redemption, righteousness, and divine love, makes his account of the afterlife fascinating, exciting and frightening. The final vision of the glory of God gives a glimpse of the majestic otherness of God and the wonder of man's destiny. This is one of C.S. Lewis's lesser known works, but as great a read as any of his better known books. A bus-load of people arrives in a sort of no-man's land between heaven and hell? – not quite the orthodox Catholic doctrine of purgatory, as people can choose heaven or hell, but with tremendous insights into that choice.

78. The Practice of the Presence of God, by Brother Lawrence (2006, Spire Books, many eds & trans; prayer /spirituality). This little book – originally written by a Carmelite lay brother living in Paris in the 17th Century – has come to be recognized by Christians of all denominations as a spiritual jewel. In a few short pages the author lays out, in the simplest language, what he considers the indispensable foundation of the spiritual life: a constant awareness of God's presence, at every moment of our existence, and a corresponding desire to do his will in even the humblest events of our everyday lives. This is a book which can be read in a few hours, but will stay with you throughout life.

79. The Screwtape Letters, by C.S. Lewis (1942, Geoffrey Bles; fiction/apologetics). This is a collection of imaginary letters from Uncle Screwtape, a senior devil, to his nephew Wormwood, who has been given his first Christian soul to tempt. Written in a gloriously funny style reminiscent of an Oxford don giving avuncular advice to a junior academic, the book nevertheless offers a candid and at times unsettling insight into the little temptations that can drag a soul from God.

80. The Snakebite Letters, by Peter Kreeft (1991, Ignatius Press). Peter Kreeft is a modern-day C.S. Lewis, so it is hardly surprising that he should attempt a work (correspondence between devils) in the style of *The Screwtape Letters*. Kreeft has the razor-sharp mind of a professor of philosophy and a certain reckless courage in ramming his arguments into the gates of hell. Advice to the junior devil Braintwister takes us on a tour of liturgy, abortion, chastity, education and the media, with truth sounding out all the more clearly as it is placed in the mouths of those who are desperately trying to conceal it.

81. True Devotion to Mary, by St Louis Marie de Montfort * (1985, Tan Books; spirituality) Perhaps the most important book ever written about Marian devotion. It teaches 'the secret of Mary', a way of living the Gospel with, by, for, and in Mary, our spiritual mother. This is de Monfort's (1673-1716) 'divine wisdom' which is the easy, short, perfect and secure way to reach heaven, our true homeland. This work of devotion was seen by its author as an inspiration from heaven, and he predicted that it would be lost for many years but would eventually have great effects in the world. After his death this book was hidden away only to be found again in 1842 in a chest of books. It has subsequently had a profound effect upon many great apostles of modern times, such as Marthe Robin, the co-foundress of the Foyers of Charity, Frank Duff, the founder of the Legion of Mary, and, of course, Pope John Paul II, who wrote that this book had marked the decisive 'turning point' in his life. It is one of those special books, which, no matter how often it is read, always seems fresh and new, and it also prophetically looks forward to a future "Age of Mary."

82. Who moved the stone? by Frank Morrison (1975, Faber and Faber). This hugely popular book was first published in 1930. It is the account of one man's intense investigation into the facts behind the events of Easter. Beginning as an agnostic on the subject Frank Morrison examines the evidence for the resurrection from a strictly unbiased position. He treats the case as a lawyer, weighing up the pros and cons, looking for a conclusion, 'beyond reasonable doubt'. To his own surprise this rigorous search for truth leads him to a conclusion that truth Himself still lives and is risen. **(P)**

Theology, teaching and faith

83. A Father Who Keeps His Promises, by Scott Hahn (1998, St Anthony Messenger Press; non-fiction). Subtitled 'God's Covenant Love in Scripture', this is a very readable work tracing the concept of 'covenant' through the Old Testament into the New. Scott Hahn is a former Presbyterian minister who converted to the Catholic Church and brought with him his immense knowledge and love of Scripture together with a desire to make it better understood as the treasure it is. Some of the sub-titles will make you laugh (or groan!) but every page is packed with interest and the result is a comprehensive and coherent picture of salvation history, which is the 'family history' of the Church.

84. Bad, Mad or God? - Proving the Divinity of Christ from St John's Gospel, by Fr John Redford (2004, St Pauls; theology). Described as the best work of apologetics since Newman's *The Grammar of Assent*, Fr John Redford's work on the historical Jesus is one of those rare things in theology – an exciting read! At a time when the majority of works on the historical Jesus are extremely sceptical about the divinity of Jesus, Fr Redford offers a refreshing exploration of the historical evidence in John's Gospel that supports the belief that Jesus is the Son of God. Fr Redford's examination of Jesus' identity and self-consciousness is so engaging because of the very orthodox presupposition that he tests – that Jesus knew Himself to be the incarnate Son of God.

85. Dare We Hope That All Men Be Saved? by Hans Urs von Balthasar (1988, Ignatius Press; theology). We do not know the outcome of the final judgment. What the New Testament teaches us, Balthasar argues, is to hope that all people will be saved. The reason we think we know that Hell is populated is because some New Testament texts seem to teach this – these he considers with great care – but also because Augustine made the mistake of thinking he definitely knew there were people there. This has distorted all subsequent reflection on the question wherever Augustine's influence has been felt. Women mystical writers taught something different, from the Middle Ages through to modern times, and their testimony strengthens Balthasar's anti-Augustinian interpretation of the New Testament.

86. Degenerate Moderns: Modernity as rationalized sexual misbehaviour, by E. Michael Jones (1993, Ignatius Press; cultural analysis). This has been justly described as a ground breaking book. The author shows how important figures like Freud and Jung rationalized their own immoral actions and proceeded to construct grand psychological theories on this basis, theories which have had a devastatingly harmful impact on Western society. It goes a long way towards explaining the moral and sexual morass Western society finds itself in. Although this is a complex area, Jones has a very readable style, and this is a book definitely worth reading. **(P)**

87. God and the Atom, by Ronald Knox (1945, Sheed and Ward, theology). Monsignor Ronald Knox, Catholic chaplain at Oxford between the wars and translator of the scriptures, was one of the greatest Catholic writers of the 20th Century. Deeply shocked after the dropping of the atomic bombs on Hiroshima and Nagasaki in August 1945, and aware of the silence of official Christian leaders, Knox speedily wrote this book questioning the act and suggesting that it signalled a new phase in humanity's false sense of power and rebellion against God. **(P)**

88. Heretics, by G K Chesterton (1905; 2006, Baronius Press; controversy/apologetics).

One of Chesterton's earliest books, written before he became a Catholic, yet thoroughly Catholic in tone, this book (originally a series of newspaper articles) sets out to challenge and rebut many of the fallacies of modern thought as represented by Chesterton's contemporary opponents – famous figures such as Frederich Nietzsche, H.G. Wells and George Bernard Shaw. Worth reading simply as a sparkling example of Chesterton's wit, it also contains some much-needed wisdom for our own days – not least the chapter 'On Certain Modern Writers and the Institution of the Family'.

89. Letters to a Young Catholic, by George Weigel (2006, Gracewing; apologetics).

In this book, Weigel takes the young Catholic on an imaginary pilgrimage around the world, stopping at various places of interest such as Chartres Cathedral and Chesterton's favourite pub to discuss different aspects of Catholic teaching and tradition. Lucid and powerfully written, Weigel manages to write passionately from the position of an older man without ever becoming sentimental or patronising. A must-read for Catholics young and old and all those interested in the Catholic faith.

90. Love Alone: The way of revelation, by Hans Urs von Balthasar (1970, Sheed and Ward; theology). This is the best short introduction to Balthasar's thought. His argument is that theological approaches beginning from the natural world (cosmology, truth) gave way to approaches beginning from the human being (anthropology, good) but that each has run into difficulties. What is needed now are approaches based on the pattern of revelation itself (love, beauty). At the centre is the love revealed in Christ crucified, the most repulsive and most compelling form or figure which moves us to faith as beauty captivates and which enables us to follow His way as love obliges the lover.

91. Love Life for Every Married Couple, by Dr Ed Wheat (rev. ed. 1997, Zondervan). Whatever your age when you come across this book, you will probably wish you had read it earlier. Dr Wheat takes us on a journey through marriage, with tact, honesty and balance, sharing many stories from his experience as a doctor and counsellor. The most remarkable aspect of the book is his belief that biblical guidelines for relationships really work, indeed that they are the only thing that works. This is definitely one to read early on, before trying every other basis for marriage and discovering that it fails.

92. Tell Me Why: A young daughter questions her father about God, by Michael Novak and Jana Novak (1998, A Lion Book; theology). Catholic theologian Michael Novak answers questions posed by his daughter, Jana, about the great matters of faith and morality, amongst others – Why does religion matter? Why are the truth claims of Catholicism more convincing than the claims of other religions? How does a modern person read the Bible? What is Christian sexual love? What is a woman's place in a Church that does not allow women priests? The fact that it is a conversation between a father and his daughter raises this dialogue above dry polemic, through their obvious mutual love, respect, and familial knowledge.

93. The Abolition of Man, by C.S. Lewis, (1943, HarperCollins, non-fiction). Another tiny book, really an essay, about education and natural law, this shows one of England's best Christian writers at his most prophetic. He manages to blow the new Eugenics movement neatly out of the water - intellectually, at least: if only it was as easy to do so in reality. Anyone concerned about genetic engineering and the effect on the world of reductionist scientism should equip themselves by reading this before they do anything else. The book is one of Pope Benedict's favourites, by the way: he quoted it for example at his talk a few years ago in Cambridge.

94. The Belief of Catholics, by Ronald Knox (1927; 2000, Ignatius Press; apologetics). A simple guide to what Catholics actually believe, written by one of the most famous converts of the 20th Century. Although possessed of a brilliant mind, Knox wears his learning lightly, and this book would be suitable for anyone who wants to learn more about the beliefs of the Catholic Church. Knox writes in a non-polemical way, seeking to instruct the honest enquirer, and (as befits a man who single-handedly produced a fresh translation of the Bible) his use of scripture when dealing with the claims of the Catholic Church will be found especially valuable.

95. The Discovery of God, by Henri de Lubac (1996, Eerdmans / T&T Clark, trans. Alexander Dru; philosophy). This is a book to dip into, not to read from front to back, partly because it is written in the form of a series of mini-essays, some only a few lines long, clustered by theme but organized as "ideas", floating in the dazzling waters of one of the wisest minds of modern times. De Lubac was the teacher of Balthasar and a leader in the movement of renewal that lead to Pope Benedict XVI. If only Richard Dawkins would read this book: it would blow away the notion he has about what Christians believe about God, and why they believe it.

96. The Spirit of the Liturgy, by Cardinal Joseph Ratzinger * (2000, Ignatius Press; theology /spirituality). One of the most lucid analyses of the meaning of the liturgy for Catholics, written while the Holy Father was in office as Prefect of the Congregation for the Doctrine of the Faith. It is beautifully written, with many inspiring thoughts for those who desire to enter more deeply into the prayer of the Church. In addition, there are rich suggestions of considerable importance for those who think they may have a vocation to study theology. His call for a renewed understanding of the liturgy is likely to be one of the hallmarks of his papacy. In a scholarly, but accessible way the author takes us through some of the most important themes in the liturgy – sacrifice, time and space, art, sign and gesture – and issues a call for a 'new liturgical movement' to renew the public worship of the Church in our own time. Required reading for anyone wanting to understand one of the driving forces of this Pontificate. This book is about much more than the Liturgy: it describes the whole history of salvation, and shows how God's purposes for each human being connect us with his plans for the whole creation. Liturgy, art, architecture, bodily worship, music, the Church's calendar. All these themes are placed in a rich biblical and theological context.

97. The Splendour of the Church, by Henri de Lubac (1999, Ignatius Press; theology). At a time when he was forbidden to teach Henri de Lubac continued to study and write. The richest fruit of that period is this reflection on the Church which anticipates substantial parts of Vatican II's constitution *Lumen gentium*. Informed by his extensive knowledge of the writings of the Fathers, as well as his concern to present a Christian view that would be both radical and contemporary, de Lubac surveys various aspects of a theology of the Church. His approach is always balanced and profound. Current thinking about the Church would benefit greatly from a fresh appropriation of the theological riches of this book.

98. Theology of the Body for Beginners, by Christopher West (2004, via Family Publications). That society has lost its way sexually is a truism. Even 'good' Catholics rejected the Church's teaching in Pope Paul VI's watershed encyclical *Humanae Vitae*. More recently John Paul II made a profound study of human sexuality, which first appeared under the title *Love and Responsibility*. Now known as the 'Theology of the Body', it is being found to point the way towards a solution of the moral problems besetting mankind. This is Christopher West's second book on the subject, written for a more popular readership.

99. We Believe, by Msgr. Alfred Gilbey (1982, St Austin Press) This short but comprehensive guide to the Catholic faith is ideal for enquiring Catholics and converts undergoing preparation. It has surely never been bettered. It is one of the many spiritual fruits of Monsignor Gilbey's work from 1932 to 1965 as Chaplain of Fisher House, the University Catholic Chaplaincy in Cambridge. With such simplicity, and yet with such density of meaning, he conveys the intellectual coherence and beauty of our faith. **(P)**

100. Writings for a Gospel Life, by Regis Armstrong (1994, St Paul's). Of the thousands of books about St Francis of Assisi, this one (by a Capuchin) must be among the finest. Armstrong provides a careful, scholarly and yet readable commentary on all the extant writings of the saint, placing them in the context of his life. The figure that emerges is a far cry from traditional piety and devotion – a deeply Catholic, deeply challenging man: certainly the closest image of Christ in the history of the Church, but one who highlights the terror as well as the joy of the Gospel.

Index of authors

Index of books